Oh me, oh my,
can it truly be?
Pickles and Pork
Rind bought an RV!

Could you imagine a wackier, sillier sight than an armadillo and elephant driving a house day and night?

Pickles and Pork Rind
Go on a Road Trip

By Crystal Cox Shimer
Illustrated by Traci Champion

Published by Argyle Fox Publishing | argylefoxpublishing.com
ISBN 978-1-953259-42-4 (Paperback)
ISBN 978-1-953259-41-7 (Hardcover)

Where will they go?
What will they do?
Will Pickles bring
his yellow
polka-dot
kazoo?

"Florida bound!" Pork Rind says and points to the map. "There's sunshine, green gators, and beaches for naps."

Next Stop:
They take North Carolina for a spin.
Blue mountains, BBQ, and a Tar Heel win!

"Hmmm . . ." Pork Rind thinks, as he scratches his head. "Where shall we go next with our rolling beds?"

Pickles perks up
with a deep Cajun drawl:
"I'd like to go south
and see Mardi Gras!"

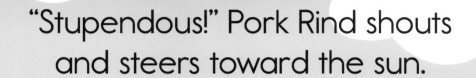

"Stupendous!" Pork Rind shouts
and steers toward the sun.

"Then off to the derby when the party's done!"

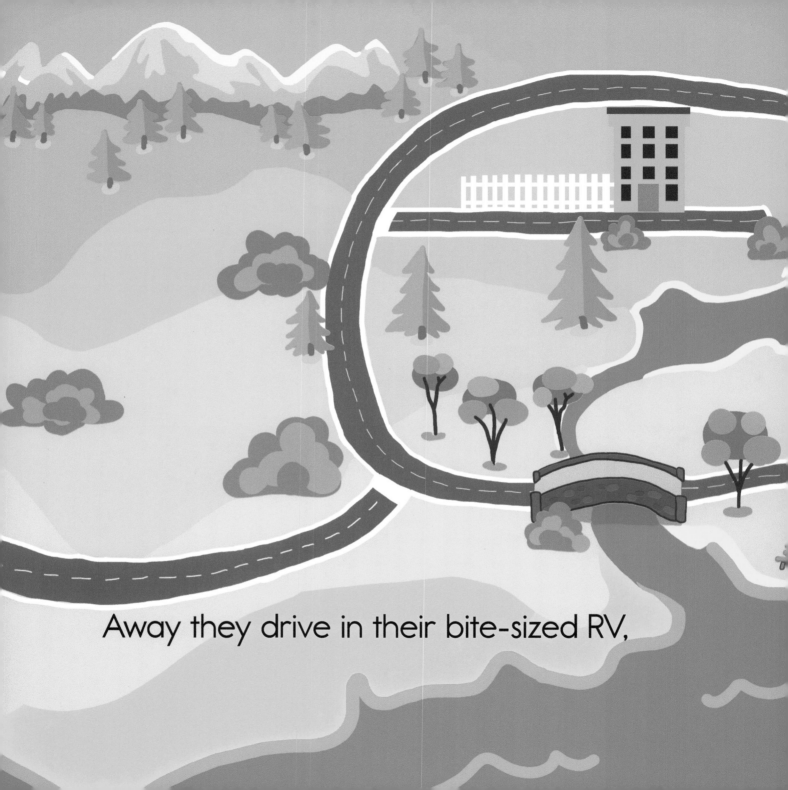

Away they drive in their bite-sized RV,

traveling
state to state
and ocean to sea.

In Kansas were sunsets
and great fields of wheat.

Arizona starred cacti, coyotes, and heat.

California brought surfing, sour bread, and big trees.

Alaska held eagles, bears,
whales, and winter freeze.

One night, while melting gooey s'mores on the fire,

they looked up at the
moon and stars to inspire.

"It's time to go home,"
Pickles said with a smile.
"What an adventure!" said Pork Rind.
"Every single mile!"

If you asked the two pals what
their favorite stops were
as they traveled the country,
the friends would concur:

Mardi Gras, 2/2016

Kentucky Derby, 5/2016

Sitka, AK, 11/2018

Started journey, 6/2015

The adventures were cool,
from east to west coast.

Yet it's not where you go,
but who you're with
that means most.

Lightning Source UK Ltd.
Milton Keynes UK
UKHW051138031222
413232UK00002B/24